MW00603408

Thank You

FOR SUPPORTING MY SMALL BUSINESS!

WE HOPE OUR PRODUCT
BRIGHTENED YOUR DAY.
YOUR SUPPORT MADE OURS!

FOR FUTURE PRODUCT
ANNOUNCEMENTS AND
DISCOUNTS FOLLOW US
ON SOCIAL MEDIA

🌐 www.gracefulbydesign.com
📷 @gracefulbydesignllc

Graceful
BY DESIGN

ELEGANT ORGANIZATION FOR EVERYDAY LIFE

Jenna

THIS BOOK BELONGS TO

_____

_____

_____

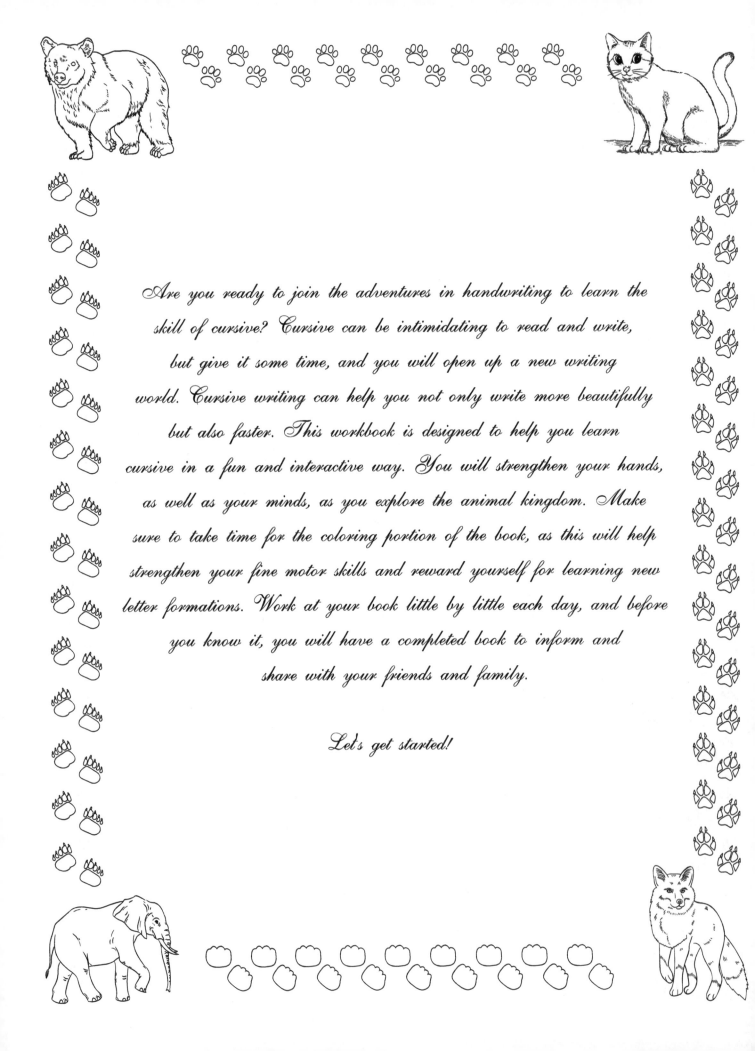

Are you ready to join the adventures in handwriting to learn the skill of cursive? Cursive can be intimidating to read and write, but give it some time, and you will open up a new writing world. Cursive writing can help you not only write more beautifully but also faster. This workbook is designed to help you learn cursive in a fun and interactive way. You will strengthen your hands, as well as your minds, as you explore the animal kingdom. Make sure to take time for the coloring portion of the book, as this will help strengthen your fine motor skills and reward yourself for learning new letter formations. Work at your book little by little each day, and before you know it, you will have a completed book to inform and share with your friends and family.

Let's get started!

Color Each Classification A Different Color

Kingdom	Very general: contains many organisms
Phylum	
Class	
Order	
Family	
Genus	
Species	Very specific: contains closely related organisms

Practice Tracing Sentence

The scientific classification system is divided into seven classifications.

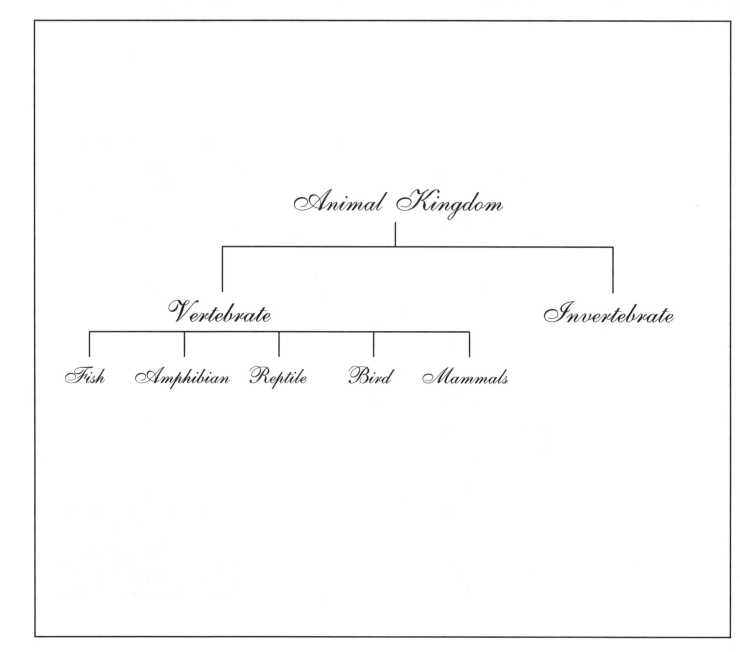

Animal Kingdom

Vertebrate   *Invertebrate*

Fish   *Amphibian*   *Reptile*   *Bird*   *Mammals*

Practice Tracing Sentence

Within the animal kingdom,
animals are separated into
two classes: invertebrates and
vertebrates.

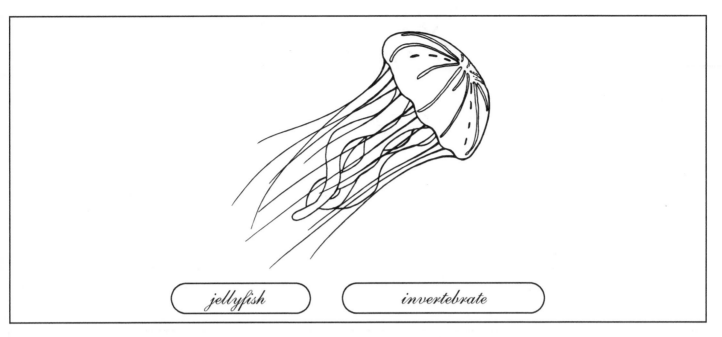

jellyfish   *invertebrate*

tiger   *vertebrate*

Practice Tracing Sentence

Invertebrates are any animal
that lacks a spine or backbone.
A vertebrate is any animal that
has a spine or backbone.

Vertebrates

Vertebrates are divided into five classes: fish, amphibians, reptiles, birds, and mammals.

fish

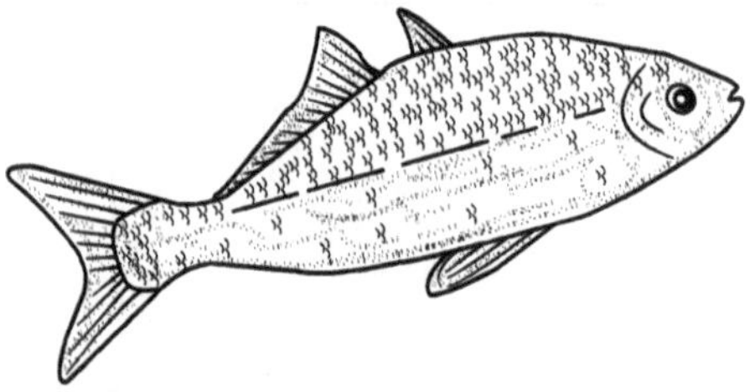

amphibian

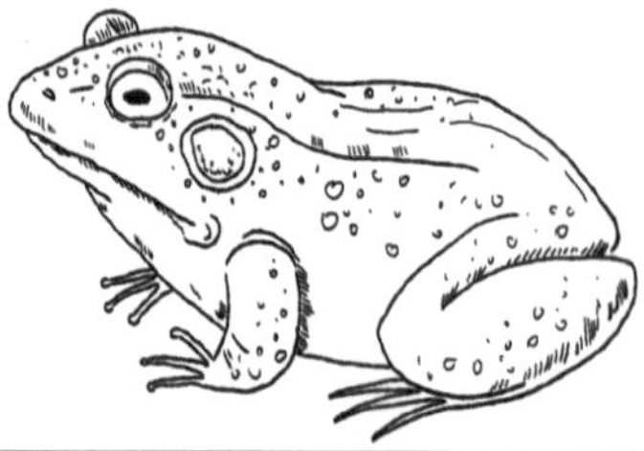

reptile

bird

mammal

Vertebrates can be cold-blooded or warm-blooded. Some vertebrates live in water, and some live on land. Amphibians live on land and in water.

Practice Connecting Letters

ba

be

bi

bo

bu

Practice Tracing Sentence

Fish are the first class of
vertebrates we will learn about.
These cold-blooded animals
can live in fresh or salt water.

Your Fish Joke To Share

What do fish take to stay
healthy? They take vitamin sea.

clown fish   fish

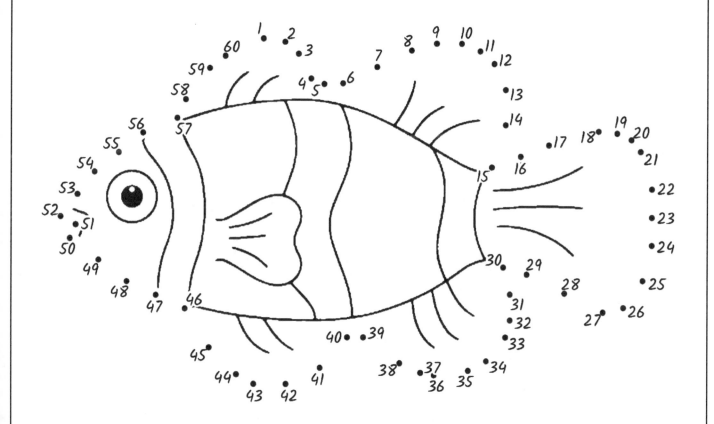

vertebrate   cold-blooded

Practice Connecting Letters

ca

ce

ci

co

cu

Practice Tracing Sentence

The whale shark is the world's
largest fish. The whale shark
can grow over fifty feet long
and weigh several tons. Each
whale shark's spot pattern
is unique.

whale shark   fish

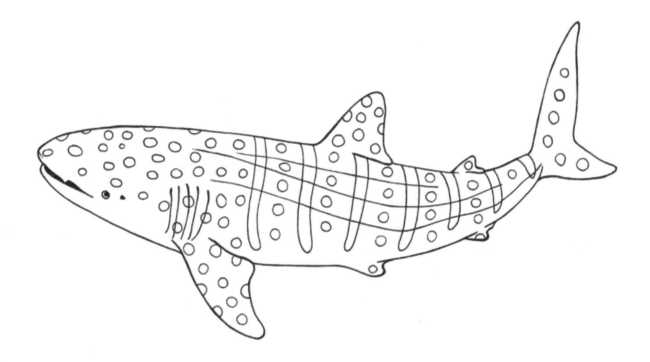

vertebrate   cold-blooded

Practice Connecting Letters

da

de

di

do

du

Practice Tracing Sentence

Did you know the sailfish
is the fastest fish in the
world? They can weigh
up to 200 pounds and
measure from six to
eleven feet in length.

sailfish   *fish*

vertebrate   cold-blooded

Practice Connecting Letters

fa

fe

fi

fo

fu

Practice Tracing Sentence

The hammerhead sharks
has exceptional 360 degree
vision due to the placement
of their eyes on their lateral
head extensions.

hammerhead shark fish

vertebrate   cold-blooded

Practice Connecting Letters

ga

ge

gi

go

gu

Practice Tracing Sentence

The spotted eagle ray can grow to over sixteen feet in length and have a nine -foot wingspan. Spotted eagle rays can leap their entire bodies out of the water!

spotted eagle ray fish

vertebrate   cold-blooded

Practice Connecting Letters

ha

he

hi

ho

hu

Practice Tracing Sentence

Amphibians can live on
water and land.

Your amphibian joke to share

What kind of shoes do
amphibians wear?
Open-toad shoes.

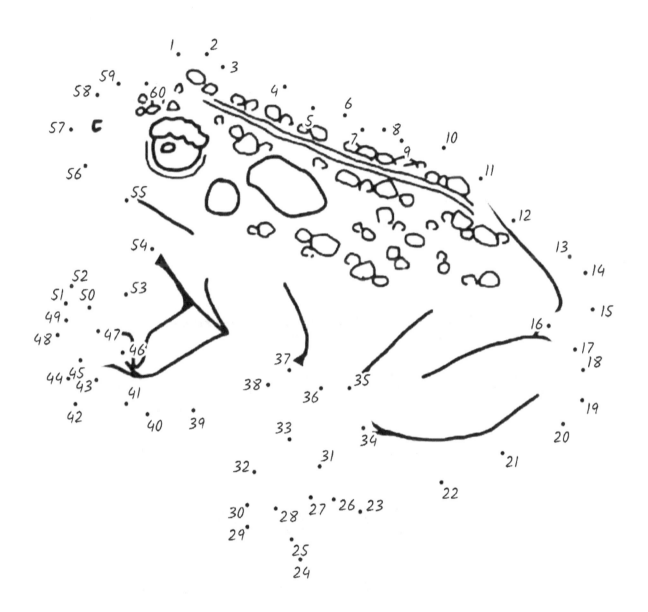

Practice Connecting Letters

ja

je

ji

jo

ju

Practice Tracing Sentence

The red-eyed tree frog is a
super climber. They have
toepads that help them to
cling to the underside of
leaves. They are nocturnal
(sleep at night).

red-eyed tree frog

amphibian

vertebrate   cold-blooded

Practice Connecting Letters

ka

ke

ki

ko

ku

Practice Tracing Sentence

Did you know a
salamander can
self-amputate (remove its
tail) if a predator attacks?
Don't worry. It can
grow back.

fire salamander

amphibian

vertebrate   cold-blooded

Practice Connecting Letters

la

le

li

lo

lu

Practice Tracing Sentence

There are many types of
toxic dart frogs. They get
their name due to the four
species that indigenous
peoples used to make
darts with their toxins.

toxic dart frog

amphibian

vertebrate   *cold-blooded*

Practice Connecting Letters

ma

me

mi

mo

mu

Practice Tracing Sentence

The fire belly newt has a red
and orange belly to serve as
a warning to predators.
They secrete toxins through
their skin that can paralyze
a predator that eats it.

fire belly newt amphibian

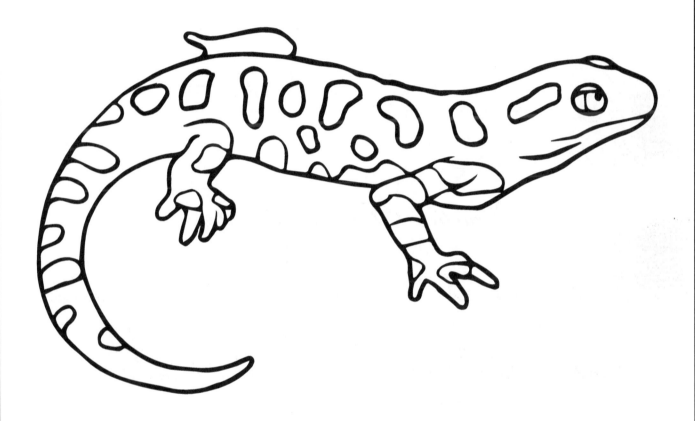

vertebrate cold-blooded

Practice Connecting Letters

na

ne

ni

no

nu

Practice Tracing Sentence

Reptiles are cold-blooded
vertebrates that breathe
air and have scaly skin.

your reptile joke to share

How does a reptile climb
a mountain? It scales it.

turtle *reptile*

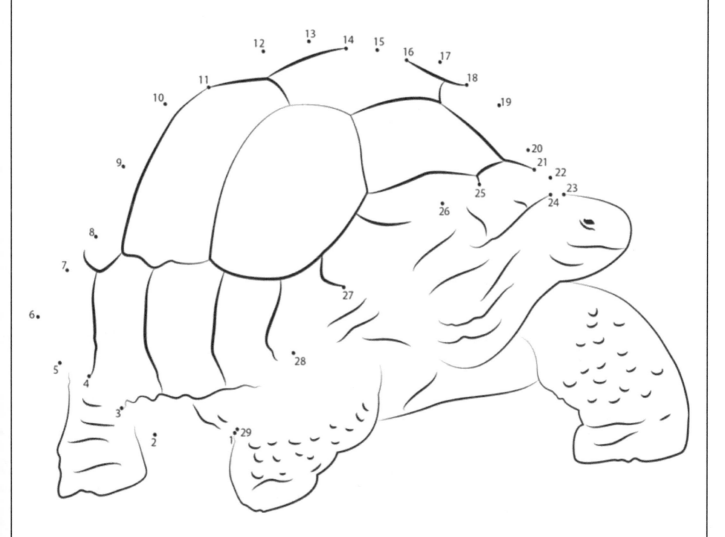

vertebrate *cold-blooded*

Practice Connecting Letters

pa

pe

pi

po

pu

Practice Tracing Sentence

The largest reptile in the
world is the saltwater
crocodile. However, this
giant reptile can't chew its
food. It swallows stones
to aid in digestion.

saltwater crocodile reptile

vertebrate cold-blooded

Practice Connecting Letters

qu

ae

ai

ao

au

Practice Tracing Sentence

The komodo dragon eats
nearly 80 percent of its
body weight in a meal!
Komodo dragons aren't
just giants; they also have
a bite that contains venom.

komodo dragon *reptile*

vertebrate *cold-blooded*

Practice Connecting Letters

ra

re

ri

ro

ru

Practice Tracing Sentence

Chameleons change their
colors due to mood or
changes in the environment.
Some chameleons can have
tongues twice as long as
their body.

chameleon

reptile

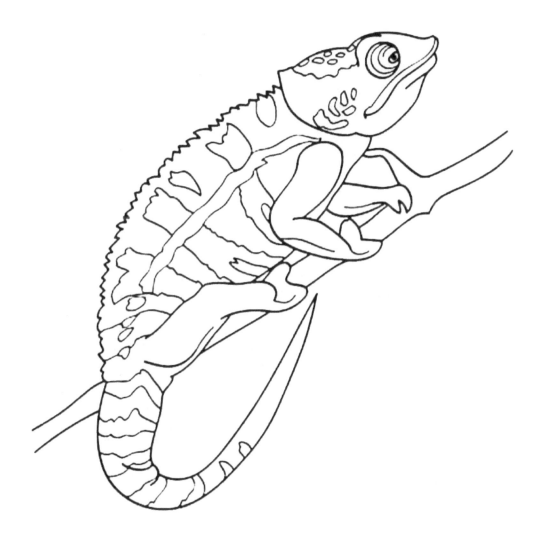

vertebrate

cold-blooded

Practice Connecting Letters

sa

se

si

so

su

Practice Tracing Sentence

The king cobra is the longest venomous snake on earth. It can spread its hood, growl or hiss to warn predators it is ready to attack.

king cobra *reptile*

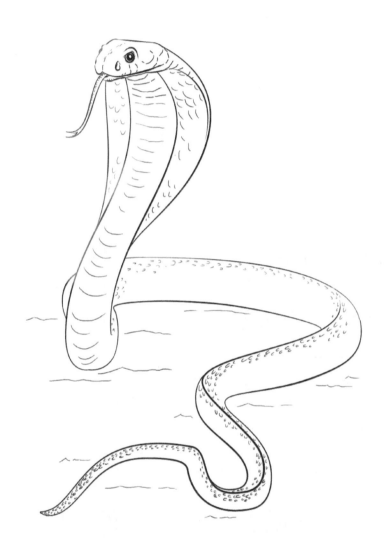

vertebrate *cold-blooded*

Practice Connecting Letters

ta

te

ti

to

tu

Practice Tracing Sentence

Birds are warm-blooded,
egg-laying vertebrates with
wings and typically fly.

Your Fish Joke To Share

What is black and white and
black and white? A penguin
falling down the stairs.

penguin   bird

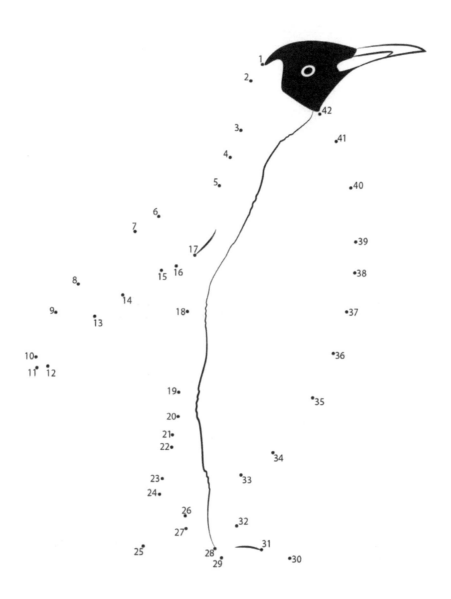

vertebrate   cold-blooded

Practice Connecting Letters

va

ve

vi

vo

vu

Practice Tracing Sentence

Time to meet the fastest bird
in the world, the peregrine
falcon. It can dive at 186
miles per hour, making it
the fastest bird and animal
in the world.

peregrine falcon   bird

vertebrate warm-blooded

wa

we

wi

wo

wu

Practice Tracing Sentence

The hummingbird species
are known for their beauty
and wing speed. They
sound similar to the wasp
because their wings can
flap 80 times in a second.

hummingbird   bird

vertebrate warm-blooded

Practice Connecting Letters

xa

xe

xi

xo

xu

Practice Tracing Sentence

Flamingos are the next bird we will look at. They have bright pink, orange, and red feathers due to their diet of shrimp. Flamingos eat with their head upside down?

flamingo   *bird*

vertebrate warm-blooded

Practice Connecting Letters

ya

ye

yi

yo

yu

Practice Tracing Sentence

This bird can have a
wingspan of over seven
feet and mates for life.
The bald eagle is an
American symbol of
freedom.

bald eagle   bird

vertebrate warm-blooded

Practice Connecting Letters

za

ze

zi

zo

zu

Practice Tracing Sentence

Mammals are warm-blooded
vertebrates with hair and nurse
their young after live births.

Your Fish Joke To Share

Did you hear about the sea
mammals that escaped the zoo?
It was otter chaos.

otter   mammal

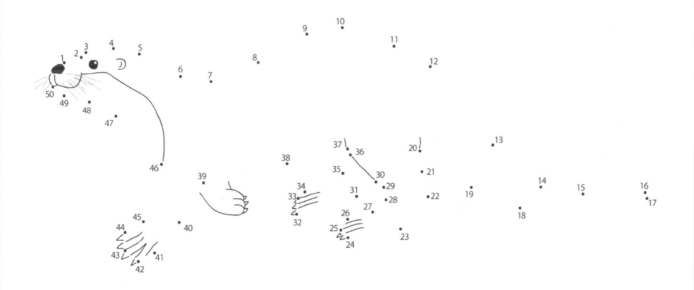

vertebrate   warm-blooded

Practice Connecting Letters

ae

ee

oa

igh

ea

Practice Tracing Sentence

The first mammal, the chimpanzee, is the most intelligent primate on earth. They communicate with each other and even create tools.

chimpanzee   mammal

vertebrate warm-blooded

Practice Connecting Letters

Ca

Ce

Ci

Co

Cu

Practice Tracing Sentence

The next mammal is also
quite intelligent, it is the
acrobatic spinner dolphin,
known to be quite playful.
Spinner dolphins can
jump 10 feet high?

spinner dolphin mammal

vertebrate warm-blooded

Practice Connecting Letters

Da

De

Di

Do

Du

Practice Tracing Sentence

The cheetah is the fastest
animal on earth. It can
run 75 miles per hour!
They have excellent vision
allowing them to spot prey
up to three miles away.

cheetah   mammal

vertebrate   warm-blooded

Practice Connecting Letters

Ga

Ge

Gi

Go

Gu

Practice Tracing Sentence

One of the strongest mammals
in the world is the grizzly
bear. The grizzly bear
typically stands seven feet
tall. Alaska has over 30,000
grizzlies living there.

grizzly bear   mammal

vertebrate warm-blooded

Practice Connecting Letters

Qu

Ae

Ai

Ao

Au

Practice Tracing Sentence

Invertebrates are also
divided into several groups.
They can live in the ocean
or on land. Invertebrates
can have many different
features and characteristics.

Invertebrate

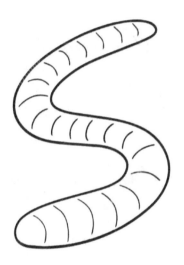

Practice Connecting Letters

Ta

Te

Ti

To

Tu

Practice Tracing Sentence

The monarch butterfly
travels around 3,000 miles
every year from Canada to
Mexico. Their bright orange
wings serve as a warning
sign to predators.

monarch butterfly insect

invertebrate cold-blooded

Practice Connecting Letters

Pa

Pe

Pu

Po

Pu

Practice Tracing Sentence

Praying mantis can see well
with their 3D vision in two
large compound eyes. They
also can rotate their head
180 degrees!

praying mantis   insect

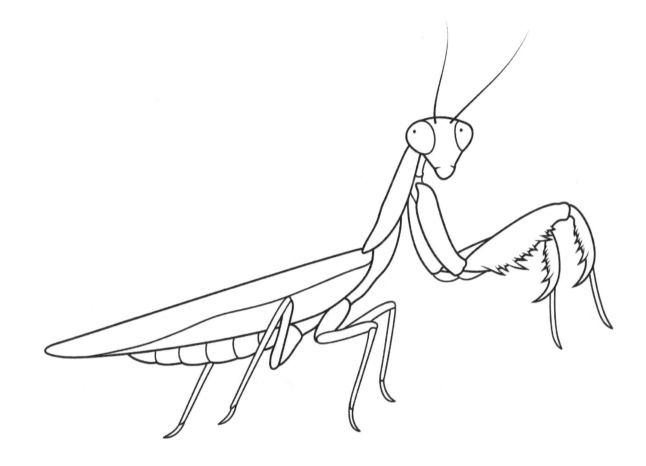

invertebrate   cold-blooded

Practice Connecting Letters

Wa

We

Wi

Wo

Wu

Practice Tracing Sentence

The longest-legged arthropod
is the Japanese spider crab.
Their legs can be longer than
12 feet! If they lose a leg
during their life, it can
regenerate a new one!

Japanese spider crab

crustacean

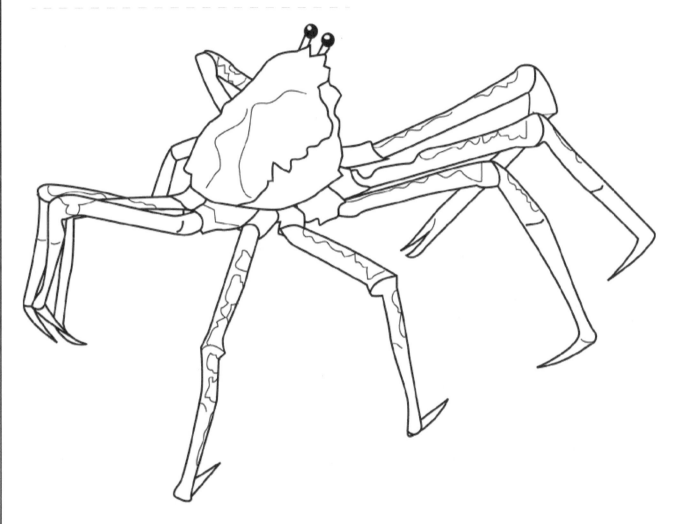

invertebrate *cold-blooded*

fa
fe
fi
fo
fu

Practice Tracing Sentence

The last invertebrate we will
learn about is a starfish. It
is not a fish. It is an
echinoderm. Starfish have
eyes and can see in the dark.

starfish   echinoderm

invertebrate   cold-blooded

Practice Connecting Letters

Ka

Ke

Ki

Ko

Ku

Practice Tracing Sentence

The tarantula spider is an
arachnid. This spider can
live for over thirty years!
They build their homes by
burrowing holes in the
ground.

tarantula   arachnid

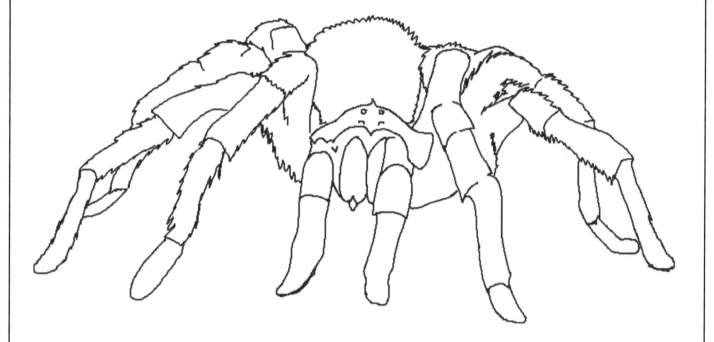

invertebrate   cold-blooded

Ja	Je	Ji	Jo	Ju
La	Le	Li	Lo	Lu
Fa	Fe	Fi	Fo	Fu
Ha	He	Hi	Ho	Hu
Ka	Ke	Ki	Ko	Ku
Ra	Re	Ri	Ro	Ru
Sa	Se	Si	So	Su
Ba	Be	Bi	Bo	Bu
Va	Ve	Vi	Vo	Vu
Ma	Me	Mi	Mo	Mu
Na	Ne	Ni	No	Nu
Ya	Ye	Yi	Yo	Yu
Xa	Xe	Xi	Xo	Xu
Za	Ze	Zi	Zo	Zu

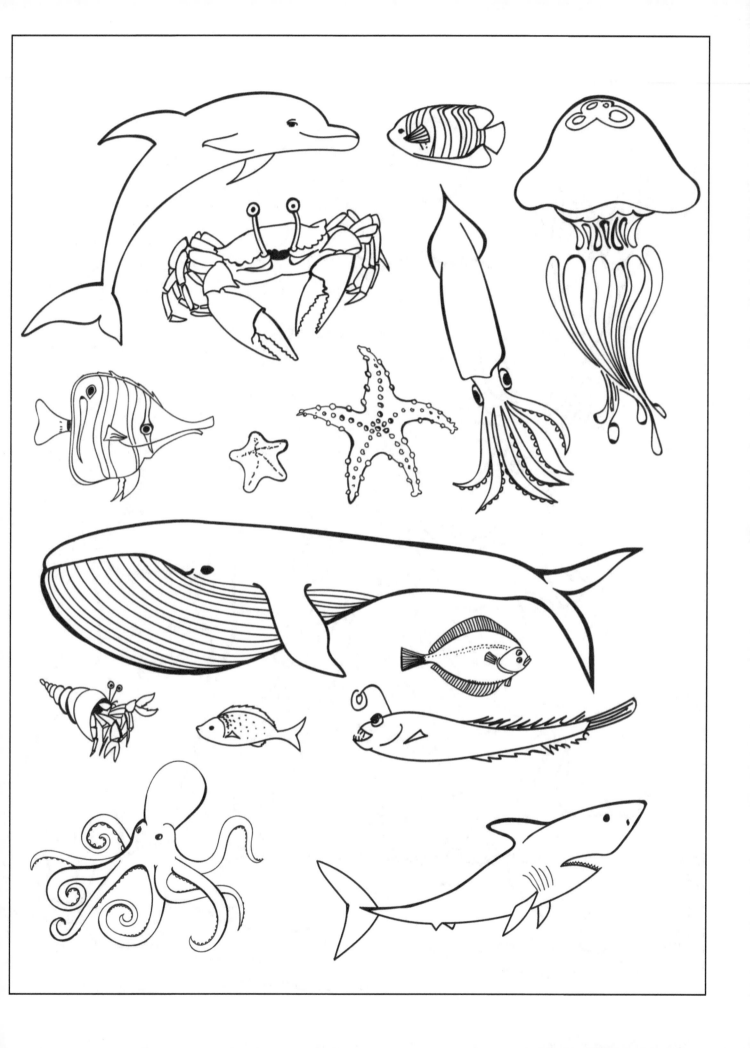

Certificate Of Achievement

THIS CERTIFICATE IS PRESENTED TO

_____

For Completing My Very Own Exploration Of
The Animal Kingdom Cursive Book

Graceful
BY DESIGN

_____   _____
TEACHER   **DATE**

18048388R00060